Popcorn
ELT
Readers

Meet ...
the animals from

Alex, Marty, Gloria and Melman ran away from New York Zoo. They went to Madagascar and Africa. Now they are going home ... with the circus!

> I'm Alex the lion and these are my friends.

Melman

> We're the penguins!

Marty

Alex

Gloria

The circus goes to different countries. Now the circus is in Monte Carlo.

Monte Carlo

Captain Dubois is from the Monte Carlo police. She works in Animal Control. She doesn't like animals.

Captain Dubois

I'm Vitaly.
I'm a tiger.

I'm Stefano.
I'm a sea lion.

Vitaly

I'm Gia.
I'm a jaguar.

Gia

Stefano

Before you read ...
What do you think? Where does the circus go next?

3

New Words

What do these new words mean? Ask your teacher or use your dictionary.

fire

She likes sitting next to the **fire**.

cannon

This is a **cannon**.

get on

Get on!

dart gun

He has a **dart gun**.

plane

The **plane** is flying.

police

They are the **police**.

ring

The lion is jumping through a **ring**.

shoot

Don't **shoot**!

train

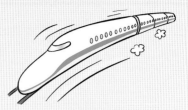

The **train** is very fast.

trapeze

They are on the **trapeze**.

'That's a lie!'

I haven't got your phone.

That's a lie!

Verbs

Present	Past
fly	flew
shoot	shot

CHAPTER ONE
'Let's go to Monte Carlo!'

It was a sunny day in Africa, but Alex wasn't happy.

'I want to go home to New York Zoo,' he said. 'Everything was easy there. Let's go to Monte Carlo! The penguins are there and they have a plane. Then we can fly home.'

'How can we go to Monte Carlo?' asked his friends.

'By sea!' answered Alex.

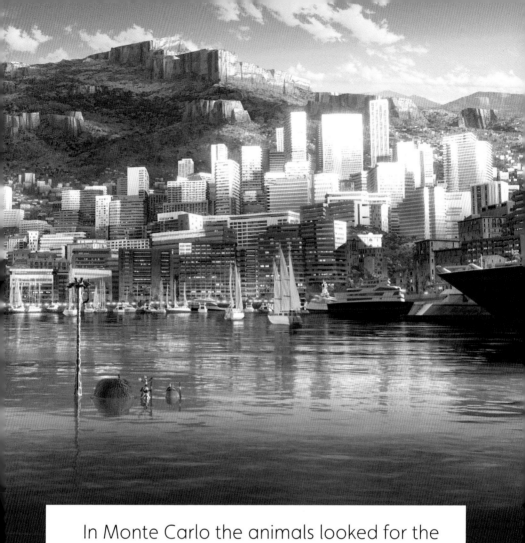

In Monte Carlo the animals looked for the penguins.

'Let's look in the casino,' said Alex. 'The penguins like money!'

But when the people in the casino saw Alex, they were very frightened.

'Look! A lion! Phone the police!' they shouted.

Captain Dubois answered the phone for the Monte Carlo police.

'Hello ... yes, this is Animal Control ... Dangerous animals? ... A lion? ... I want a lion's head in my room!' she said. 'I'm coming now with my dart gun!'

Dubois went to the casino.

'I want that lion's head!' she shouted.

Suddenly the animals saw the penguins and their old plane.

'Quick!' shouted the penguins. 'Get on!'

They all jumped on the plane.

'Goodbye!' shouted Alex.

'I'm coming after you!' shouted Dubois.

CHAPTER TWO
The circus train

The animals were on the old plane and they were happy. 'New York, New York!' the animals started singing. 'We're going home!'

'No, we're not!' said the penguins. 'We've got a problem with the plane.'

CRASH! The plane came down.

'What are we going to do?' said Marty.

'Look, there's a train!' said Alex. 'Let's get on!'

A door on the train opened. The animals saw a big tiger.

'Go away!' he said. 'This is a circus train. YOU'RE not circus animals!' He closed the door.

The door opened again. This time they saw a sea lion and a jaguar.

'Help us!' said Alex. 'We ARE circus animals!'

'OK,' said Stefano the sea lion. 'Get on!'

⏸

Alex, his friends and the penguins all jumped on the train.

'Look, Vitaly!' said Stefano. 'Some famous American circus animals!'

Vitaly the tiger wasn't happy. 'Are you famous circus animals?' he asked.

'Yes, yes, of course,' said Alex quickly. 'So where are you going?'

'We're going to Rome and London, and then maybe we're going to New York,' said Stefano.

'New York!' said Alex. 'That's our home!'

Captain Dubois and the police looked for the animals.

'They're on a train,' said Dubois. 'I know it!'

But the circus train and the animals were far away now.

CHAPTER THREE
The ring of fire

The circus went to Rome. 'This is going to be exciting,' said Alex. 'There are a lot of people here.'

But the circus wasn't exciting and the people weren't happy. 'We want our money back!' they shouted.

Captain Dubois went to Rome too. She looked at a police computer. She found a picture of Alex when he was in New York Zoo.

'You can run away from the zoo,' she thought, 'but you can't run away from me!'

Alex talked to the circus animals. 'Listen,' he said. 'This circus is no good. It's not exciting.'

'It wasn't always bad,' said Stefano. 'Vitaly was very famous. Everyone came to see him. He jumped through a ring of fire. But every day he wanted the ring to be smaller and smaller.'

Stefano looked at Alex. 'One day he couldn't go through the ring,' he said. 'The fire was terrible. He is not the same tiger now. He is frightened.'

'Can you help us, Alex?' Stefano asked. 'You're a famous American circus animal.'

'I don't know ...' said Alex.

'Please!' said Stefano.

'OK,' said Alex.

Alex and his friends had a lot of new ideas for the circus. Marty helped Stefano with the circus cannon. Alex and Gia learned to fly on the trapeze. Melman and Gloria danced. But Vitaly wasn't happy. He didn't want to go through the ring of fire again.

The circus moved to London.

'It's going to be wonderful,' said Alex. 'Vitaly is going to be great!'

But Stefano started crying. 'Vitaly is going away,' he said.

Alex found Vitaly. 'Please don't go,' he said. 'Only you can jump through a ring of fire.'

'I don't know …' Vitaly said.

'But the circus needs you,' said Alex.

'OK,' said Vitaly. 'One more jump for my friends.'

This time the circus was exciting. Marty and
Stefano flew from the circus cannon. Alex and
Gia flew on the trapeze.

'And NOW!' said Stefano. 'Vitaly the tiger is
going to jump through this small ring.'

'No one can do that!' thought the people.

'Fire, please, Stefano!' shouted Vitaly. He ran ...
and jumped through the ring of fire.

'Wow!' said the people. 'We love this circus!'

Captain Dubois found the circus animals in London.

'Look at this picture,' she said. 'Alex is not a circus lion! He's from New York Zoo!'

The circus animals looked at the picture. Then they looked at Alex.

'You're not famous American circus animals!' said Stefano. 'That's a lie!'

'I'm sorry,' said Alex. 'We wanted to go home.'

The penguins saw Dubois. 'Stop her!' they said.

They put Dubois in the cannon. BANG!

CHAPTER FOUR
Home again!

The circus went to New York.

'Home!' shouted Alex.

But when the animals saw the zoo, they didn't go in.

'It's very small,' said Marty.

'Yes,' said Alex. 'The circus was more exciting.'

Dubois went to New York Zoo too. She saw the animals.

'You are mine now!' she laughed and she shot them with her dart gun.

The people from the zoo saw Captain Dubois. They were very happy to see their animals again.

'You found our animals!' they said. 'Thank you, Captain Dubois!'

It was circus time in New York but Stefano was not happy. He started to cry.

'We need our friends from the zoo,' he said. 'It's not the same now.'

Suddenly the penguins came in.

'Look!' the penguins shouted. 'We found this dart near the zoo. It's a dart from Captain Dubois's gun. We must go and help our friends!'

'Wake up, Alex!' shouted the people.

Alex opened his eyes. He was back in the zoo. 'Oh no!' he thought.

Then he saw Captain Dubois. 'I want that lion's head!' shouted Dubois.

Suddenly the circus animals came to help. 'Stop her!' they shouted and they jumped on Dubois. 'This woman is dangerous. Let's put HER in the zoo!' they laughed.

'Thank you!' said Alex.

'What are you all going to do now?' asked Gia.

'I don't know. But I like flying from the cannon,' said Marty.

'And we like dancing,' said Gloria and Melman.

'We don't want to go back to the zoo,' said Alex. 'Can we come with you?'

'Of course!' said Stefano.

'WE LOVE THE CIRCUS!' the animals shouted.

THE END

THE CIRCUS

Everyone loves the circus! But when was the first circus? And how was it different from the circus today?

The first circus

The circus started in Ancient Greece and Rome more than 2000 years ago. It was very different from the circus today. One of the first circuses was the Circus Maximus near Rome. People could watch chariot races there.

chariot race

acrobat

Did you know...?

The word 'circus' comes from the Greek word for a circle: *kirkos*.

The Big Top

Modern circuses started in the 1700s. They moved from place to place. In 1825, an American circus made the first circus tent or 'Big Top'.

Around the world

There were famous circuses in many countries. In the USA, people liked to see animals do tricks. The Chinese circus was famous for its acrobats.

The circus today

In the 1960s and 1970s, people didn't always want to see wild animals in the circus. Today some famous circuses have no animals. The *Cirque du Soleil* has acrobats and jugglers from a lot of different countries.

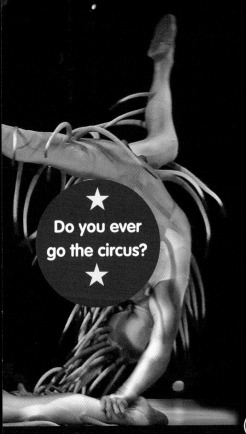

★ Do you ever go the circus? ★

What do these words mean? Find out.

circle   tent   trick
wild   juggler

After you read

1 True (✓) or False (✗)? Write in the box.

a) The penguins were in Monte Carlo. ✓

b) The plane came down in London. ☐

c) The circus in Rome was very good. ☐

d) Marty helped Stefano with the cannon. ☐

e) Gloria was on the trapeze with Alex. ☐

f) Dubois went to New York too. ☐

g) The animals were happy when they saw the zoo. ☐

2 Answer the questions.

a) Who went to Monte Carlo by plane? the penguins

b) Who found a picture of Alex? ....

c) Who danced in the circus? ....

d) Who jumped through the ring of fire? ....

e) Who put Dubois in the cannon? ....

f) Who shot Alex with a dart gun? ....

Where's the popcorn?
Look in your book.
Can you find it?

Puzzle time!

1 Match the places.

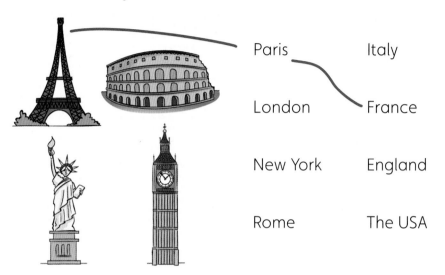

Paris   Italy

London   France

New York   England

Rome   The USA

2 Answer the questions. Tick your favourites and then ask your friends.

Which do you like best?

a) the circus   ☐ ☐ ☐ ☐ ☐

     or

     the zoo   ☐ ☐ ☐ ☐ ☐

b) trains   ☐ ☐ ☐ ☐ ☐

     or

     planes   ☐ ☐ ☐ ☐ ☐

3 Find the names of the animals.

a) ....tiger.... b) .... c) ....

d) .... e) ....

4 Write the missing letters. Now use the letters to complete the address on the postcard.

Dear Friends,

I am in New York with Marty, Melman a nd Gloria. We _ re in the circu _ . It is very exciting! We went to _ onte C arlo. Then we went to _ ome by tr _ in. After that we went to Lon _ on. It was _ reat!

Lots of love,

_ lex

THE ANIMALS

_ a _ _ _ _ _ _ c _ _ _

NEAR AFRICA

Imagine ...

1 Work in small groups. Choose one of these pictures. Imagine you are the characters and write a dialogue.

2 Act out your dialogue for your friends.

Chant

1 🎧 **Listen and read.**

The circus chant

'Let's go!' said Alex. 'I want to go home.'
The animals went with the circus to Rome.
But Captain Dubois was not far behind.
'Stop!' she said. 'That lion is mine!'

The animals went with their circus friends.
London … New York … Home again!
They saw the zoo, but it was very small.
'It's not good,' said Alex. 'Not good at all'.

Dubois shot Alex and his friends too,
Then the circus animals put HER in the zoo.
'Thank you!' said Alex. 'Now what can we do?'
'We love the circus! We're coming with you!'

2 🎧 **Say the chant.**